P9-DWI-051

© 2012 Age of Learning, Inc.

Published by Age of Learning, Inc., P.O. Box 10458, Glendale, California 91209.
No part of this work may be reproduced in whole or in part, or stored in a retrieval system,
or transmitted in any form or by any means, electronic, mechanical, photocopying,
recording, or otherwise, without written permission of the publisher.
Age of Learning, and associated logos are trademarks and/or
registered trademarks of Age of Learning, Inc.

Library of Congress Control Number: 2012912298
A Toy for Spot/Age of Learning, Inc.
Summary: In this Word Family Beginning Reader, Scot and Dot play a game of
Cold and Hot with their dog, Spot.

ISBN: 978-1-62116-008-3

21 20 19 18 17 16 15 14 13 12   1 2 3 4 5
Printed in the U.S.A, on 10% recycled paper. ♻
First printing, August 2012

A Toy for Spot

Age of Learning, Inc., Glendale, California
This book is also available at **ABCmouse.com**, the award-winning early learning online curriculum.
Find free apps at **ABCmouse.com/apps**.

This is Scot,
and this is Dot.
They have a pet.
His name is Spot.

Dot is a girl.
Scot is a boy.
Spot is a dog.
Spot has a toy.

Scot and Dot got
the toy for Spot.
Spot likes the toy
he got a lot!

Scot hides the toy
in a big blue pot.
They play a game
of *Cold and Hot*.

Where is the toy?
Is it under the cot?
Spot looks there.

"You are cold!"
says Scot.

Where is the toy?
Is the toy by Dot?
Spot looks there.

"You are warm!"
says Scot.

Where is the toy?
Is it in the pot?
Spot goes there.
Now he is hot!

Spot looks in
the big blue pot.
He gives the toy
to Scot and Dot.

Will they stop?
No, they will not!
Spot wants to
play more *Cold
and Hot!*

The End

CONTRA COSTA COUNTY LIBRARY

3 1901 05894 9324